ANNE GEDDES

*Down in the Garden*

# Journal

ANNE GEDDES ™

ISBN-1-55912-344-3

© 1996 Anne Geddes

Published in 1996 by Cedco Publishing Company
2955 Kerner Blvd., San Rafael, CA 94901

Seventh Printing, July 1997

Designed by Jane Seabrook
Produced by Kel Geddes
Typeset by Image Design
Images first published in *Down in the Garden*.
Color separations by Image Centre
Printed by South China Printing Co. Ltd., Hong Kong

Please write to us for a FREE FULL COLOR catalog of our fine Anne Geddes calendars
and books, Cedco Publishing Company, 2955 Kerner Blvd., San Rafael, CA 94901.

Welcome to the world of Anne Geddes.

The images used in this journal are taken from Anne's latest collective work entitled *Down In The Garden*.

Anne says in her foreword to that book:
"I hope that, through my work as a photographer, I have been able to pass on my appreciation of the beauty and charm of little children. As adults we all need to stop occasionally and look at ourselves and our circumstances with an open mind and a sense of humor, and remember to appreciate the simple things in life, which are often the most important."

We hope that when using this journal you can record some of the simple, yet magic, moments of your life's journey.

Canterbury Belles